FOLK HEROES

PAUL BUNYAN

Sandra Becker

WEIGL PUBLISHERS INC.

Published by Weigl Publishers Inc.
123 South Broad Street, Box 227
Mankato, MN 56002 USA
Web site: www.weigl.com

Library of Congress Cataloging-in-Publication Data

Becker, Sandra.
  Paul Bunyan / Sandra Becker.
      p. cm. -- (Folk heroes)
Includes index.
Summary: An introduction to the life and accomplishments of the
fictional folk hero, Paul Bunyan, who is said to have created the
logging industry in America.
  ISBN 1-59036-076-1 (alk. paper)
  1. Bunyan, Paul, (Legendary character)--Legends. [1. Bunyan, Paul,
(Legendary character)--Legends. 2. Folklore--United States. 3. Logging.
4. Tall tales.] I. Title. II. Series.
  PZ8.1.B3883 Pau 2003
  [398.2]--dc21

                          2002012322

Printed in the United States of America
1 2 3 4 5 6 7 8 9 0 06 05 04 03 02

Photograph Credits
Every reasonable effort has been made to trace ownership and to obtain permission to reprint copyright
material. The publishers would be pleased to have any errors or omissions brought to their attention so
that they may be corrected in subsequent printings.
Cover: Illustration of Paul Bunyan (Kate McKeon), Background photo (Corel Corporation); **Ray Bang,
Minnesota Historical Society:** page 21; **Courtesy Bemidji Visitors & Convention Bureau:** page 19L;
W.E. LaFountain, Minnesota Historical Society: page 18; **Kate McKeon:** pages 3, 7, 9, 11, 13, 14, 15;
Minnesota Historical Society: page 22; **Photo 24/David Skernick:** page 5; **Walt Disney/Photofest:** pages
17, 19R.

Project Coordinator Tina Schwartzenberger **Copy Editor** Frances Purslow
Design & Layout Terry Paulhus & Virginia Boulay **Photo Researcher** Nicole Bezic King

Contents

A Logging Legend

Paul Bunyan is a fictional folk hero. This means that he was not real. It is not known how the **legend** of Paul Bunyan began, but many people believe that **loggers** invented him. After chopping down trees all day, loggers often sat around campfires telling stories. These stories were passed along over time. People started to think that these stories were true. Paul Bunyan stories were about logging. Each time a Paul Bunyan story was told by a new storyteller, extra details were added. Every new story would be more incredible than the last one.

i FACT FILE

The legends of Paul Bunyan began to spread in the 1800s. Stories were told by ordinary working people. Some people spoke as if they knew Paul Bunyan.

PAUL BUNYAN
WELCOMES YOU TO THE
TREES OF MYSTERY
KLAMATH, CALIFORNIA
WEIGHT 30,000 LBS   CONCRETE BASE 600,000 LBS
HEIGHT 49 FEET 2 IN.   WAIST 52 FEET AROUND
AXE 24 FEET LONG   CHEST 66 FEET AROUND
                          BOOTS
DESIGNED BY
ANN COOPER

Paul Bunyan statues can be found
across the United States, including
Arizona, California, and Minnesota.

Sleeping Giant

Some stories claim that Paul Bunyan was born in Maine. Other stories place his birth somewhere in Canada. Paul Bunyan was a very large baby, weighing between 80 and 100 pounds at birth. When Paul was 3 weeks old, he rolled over in his sleep and destroyed 4 miles of forest. After that, Paul's parents made him a cradle out of wood. They placed the cradle in the town's **harbor**. Floating in his cradle, the giant baby began to rock back and forth. Large waves caused by the rocking flooded small towns.

i | FACT FILE

Paul became a very large and strong man when he grew up. His size and strength made him an excellent logger.

When Paul Bunyan was a baby, his cradle caused large waves as it rocked.

Paul Across America

Paul Bunyan was a hero of the wilderness. Many of his legendary deeds explain the creation of America's natural wonders. One story tells how Paul used a **glacier** to scoop out Washington's Puget Sound, an arm of the Pacific Ocean. In another tale, Paul dug the Great Lakes, forming Lake Superior, Lake Michigan, Lake Huron, Lake Erie, and Lake Ontario. The lakes were used as drinking holes by Babe, his big, blue ox. Other tales describe how Paul formed many of the rivers and mountain ranges in the United States.

i FACT FILE

Paul Bunyan stories are among the best-known **tall tales**. The tall tales about Paul Bunyan often explained the natural wonders of the United States.

One legend tells of how Paul dropped his ax, cutting the Grand Canyon out of the ground.

Amazing Abilities

Paul's strength made him an excellent logger. He could chop down trees with great speed. Paul's ax was so large and heavy that it took seven men to lift it. The handle of Paul's ax was actually an oak tree.

Paul could move quickly. At night, he could blow out a candle and be under his bed covers before the flame had stopped burning. Other tales were just as incredible. For instance, Paul once shot a bear and raced ahead to see if the bullet had hit the animal. He ran so quickly that he arrived before the bullet. The bullet struck Paul's backside.

i FACT FILE

In some legends, Paul Bunyan was the inventor of logging. The logging industry was important to the **settlement** of the United States. The forests were full of trees, and the **timber** could be sold to other countries.

Paul could cut down 100 trees with one swing of his ax.

The Look of a Legend

Paul was a man of great size. One legend describes Paul as being so large that ordinary people could only reach his ankles. He had a loud, thundering voice. People said that every time Paul sneezed, he blew the roof off his house.

ACTIVITY

People's clothing can say a great deal about them. What do Paul's clothes say about him? Why was it important for Paul to carry an ax? How did his boots help him travel through the forests? What would you wear if you worked in the outdoors in the 1800s? Think about why each clothing item would be important to a logger.

Paul combed his beard with the top of a fir tree.

Paul's watch was actually a clock from a courthouse building. The watch hung from a logging chain that dangled from a pocket.

Paul bent an iron bar into the shape of a safety pin and used it for a rip in his pants.

Paul's boots left prints that were the size of small lakes.

Paul's ax was as wide as a barn door. Legends tell that Paul invented the double-bladed ax. Chopping down trees with a double-bladed ax was much faster and easier.

Paul's Pals

One legend describes how Paul and Babe, the blue ox, met. Paul found Babe in a snowdrift. Babe was so cold that he had turned blue. Paul blew three warm breaths on Babe. The ox came back to life. Babe grew and became very large. He could eat thirty bales of hay for a snack. Babe stayed blue forever.

Ole was a legendary **blacksmith**. He was the only blacksmith who could make iron shoes large enough for Babe. Babe's shoes used a great amount of iron. A new iron **mine** had to be opened every time Ole made shoes for the giant ox.

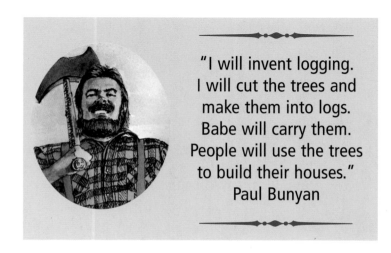

"I will invent logging. I will cut the trees and make them into logs. Babe will carry them. People will use the trees to build their houses."
Paul Bunyan

Babe was Paul's best friend.

Spreading Stories

James MacGillivray was the first person to record the stories of Paul Bunyan. He wrote the stories for a Detroit newspaper in 1910. A few years later, a lumber company used the legend of Paul Bunyan to sell its timber. Since then, ballets, plays, cartoons, movies, and children's books have been made about Paul Bunyan.

Disney made a short movie about Paul Bunyan. In the movie, Paul and Babe travel across America. They create Pikes Peak in Colorado and the Missouri River.

"In the old days, there were men (in logging camps) who could tell Paul Bunyan stories evening after evening for weeks together and never repeat themselves."
A Logger

Disney made a short film about American legend Paul Bunyan in 1958.

The Trail of Tales

1916 Collections of Paul Bunyan tales are first published as books.

1860s Stories of Paul are told in logging camps. The stories quickly spread throughout Michigan, Wisconsin, and Minnesota.

1850s Settlement increases in the United States. Logging camps are built to produce lumber for buildings.

1914 A lumber company gives away booklets with stories and cartoons about the legendary Paul Bunyan.

1910 James MacGillivray is the first person to write stories about Paul in a newspaper.

1837 A story spreads about how Paul Bunyan fought against Queen Victoria's army in England. The legend tells he came to the United States to find work after the war.

1958 Disney makes a cartoon based on the stories of Paul Bunyan.

1937 Bemidji, Minnesota, erects statues of Paul Bunyan and Babe.

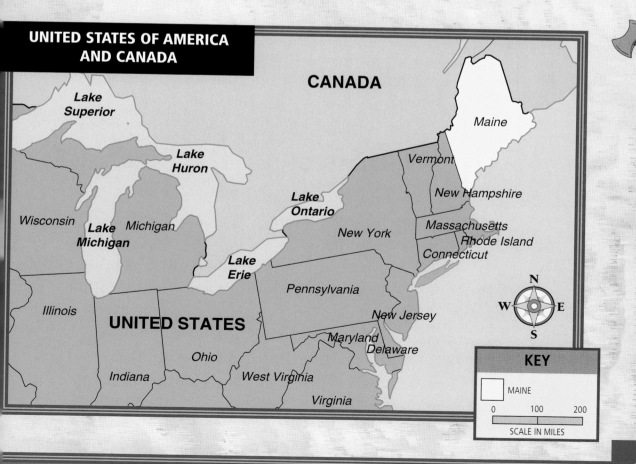

UNITED STATES OF AMERICA AND CANADA

CANADA

Lake Superior

Lake Huron

Maine

Vermont

Lake Ontario

New Hampshire

Wisconsin

Lake Michigan

Michigan

New York

Massachusetts

Rhode Island

Connecticut

Lake Erie

Illinois

Pennsylvania

UNITED STATES

New Jersey

Maryland

Ohio

Delaware

Indiana

West Virginia

Virginia

N
W E
S

KEY

MAINE

0   100   200

SCALE IN MILES

More Tales to Tell

Paul Bunyan is one of the country's best-loved folk heroes. Many books and Web sites honor this folk hero's skills and creations. To learn more about Paul, you can borrow books from the library or surf the Internet.

Books

Learn more about how Paul met Babe by reading: Gregg, Andy. *Paul Bunyan and the Winter of the Blue Snow*. Spring Lake: River Road Publications, 2000.

Read about popular American tall tales in: Berger, Melvin. *Paul Bunyan and Other Tall Tales*. New York: Scholastic, Inc., 2002.

Web Sites

Encarta Homepage
www.encarta.com
Type terms such as "folklore" and "Paul Bunyan" into the site's search engine to learn more about folk heroes, including Paul Bunyan.

Paul Bunyan Trail Tall Tale
www.paulbunyantrail.com/talltale.html
Read an illustrated story of Paul Bunyan.

Examine and Explain

Legendary folk heroes, such as Paul Bunyan, remind us of the hard work and special skills of the people who settled the United States. Using the library and the Internet, research more tall tales about Paul Bunyan's size, strength, skills, and creations. Design a **brochure** for a fictional company. Use these Paul Bunyan tales to sell certain features or products of your company.

What Have You Learned?

Test your knowledge of Paul Bunyan by answering the following questions.

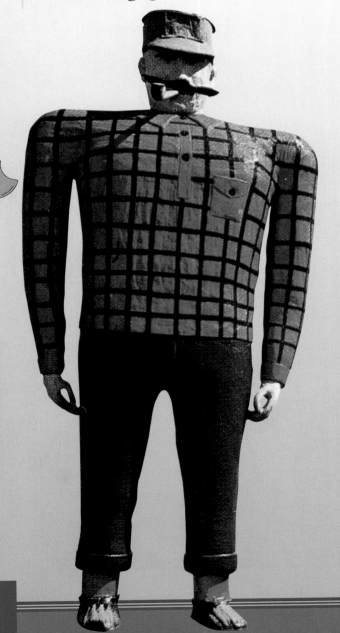

1 **True or False?**
Paul Bunyan was a real person.

2 **True or False?**
James MacGillivray was the first person to write the stories of Paul Bunyan in a newspaper.

3 **True or False?**
Paul Bunyan created the Grand Canyon.

4 **True or False?**
Paul Bunyan tales were first told in the 1790s.

5 What was Ole's job in the logging camp?
a) lumberjack
b) cook
c) blacksmith
d) bookkeeper

6 Why were tall tales important to American history?
a) They share the American sense of fun.
b) They help us remember the people who settled the United States.
c) They describe the history of United States.
d) They are interesting stories.

7 Why was the legendary Paul Bunyan so large and strong?
a) His size and strength scared people.
b) His size and strength made Paul seem more important.
c) People only like folk heroes who were big and strong.
d) Logging was hard and heavy work.

8 Why are the stories of Paul Bunyan considered to be legends?
a) Paul Bunyan stories explain how natural wonders were formed.
b) Paul Bunyan tales are not popular.
c) Paul Bunyan stories cannot be proven to be true.
d) Paul Bunyan is known throughout the United States.

9 What did Paul use to comb his hair?
a) the top of a fir tree
b) a comb
c) a brush
d) his fingers

10 Why was Babe blue?
a) He fell into a tub of ink.
b) He was frozen blue in a snowdrift.
c) He ate so many blueberries that he turned blue.
d) He was born blue.

ANSWERS

10. b)
9. a)
8. c)
7. d)
6. b)
5. c)
4. False. Paul Bunyan stories began to spread in the 1800s.
3. False. Paul Bunyan was a fictional character. The story describing how Paul created the Grand Canyon did not really happen.
2. True
1. False. It is believed that loggers created the legend of Paul Bunyan.

23

Words to Know

blacksmith: a person who makes tools out of iron

brochure: a small paper book that gives information

glacier: a mass of ice that never completely melts

harbor: water near the shoreline where boats are docked

legend: a popular story that cannot be proven to be true

loggers: people who cut, prepare, and carry lumber

mine: an area where minerals are taken from the earth

settlement: making a home in a new country

tall tales: exaggerated stories

timber: wood used to build things

Index